The Music of
THE
WORK
AND THE
GLORY

Music by
Lynn S. Lund

Lyrics by
Gerald N. Lund

BOOKCRAFT
Salt Lake City, Utah

"The Work and the Glory," " This I Know,"
" A Marvelous Work," and "Praise to the Man"
are available as sheet music from
Jackman Music Corp., 1-800-950-1900.

ISBN 1-57008-188-3

Second Printing, 1995

Printed in the United States of America

CONTENTS

Lyrics by Gerald N. Lund / Music by Lynn S. Lund and Merrill Jenson

In preparation for the return of Jesus Christ as King of kings and Lord of lords, God began the great work of restoration in the spring of 1820. Like the stone cut out of the mountain without hands, the kingdom of God has rolled onward from that simple beginning until today it is found in more than one hundred fifty countries. "This is my work and my glory," God declared, "to bring to pass the immortality and eternal life of man" (Moses 1:39). The series *The Work and the Glory* and this album celebrate the grand and glorious work which the Father has set in place and which we now see unfolding.

Lyrics adapted by Gerald N. Lund from Joseph Smith—History 1:14-17 /
Music by Lynn S. Lund

Troubled by conflicting cries of which church was right, and deeply desirous of knowing God's will in the matter, a young boy of fourteen left a small log home and walked a few hundred yards west to a thick grove of trees. It was such a simple act. It would have such profound consequences. Even the powers of darkness understood the significance of what was about to happen and sought to intervene. But God's purposes were not to be thwarted. In one blazing shaft of revelation, not only would the young Joseph get his answer, but the world would be changed forever. (Vol. 1, pp. 48-60.)

Lyrics by Gerald N. Lund / Music by Lynn S. Lund

When Benjamin Steed brings his family to western New York and settles in Palmyra Township in the fall of 1826, they soon learn of Joseph Smith and his report of remarkable events. Nathan Steed, the second son, listens, believes, and accepts almost immediately. Others in the community react far differently. Influenced by the deep and bitter opposition of her own father, Lydia McBride rejects the whole idea of Joseph Smith and his claims of heavenly manifestations. When she and Nathan fall in love, these vastly divergent feelings about Joseph and his mission threaten to tear them apart. Nathan pleads with her to make an honest search. Lydia's father adamantly forbids her to do so. Torn between her love for her family and her love for Nathan, Lydia finally decides that she cannot let either of them make the decision for her. She decides that she must come to know for herself. (Vol. 1, pp. 433-35.)

LORD, MAKE US ONE   *22*
Mary Ann

Lyrics by Gerald N. Lund / Music by Lynn S. Lund

The story of the Restoration becomes a great divisive force within the Steed family, as well as within the community. Like her son Nathan, Mary Ann Morgan Steed soon comes to completely believe that Joseph Smith has been called of God. Benjamin Steed, a hardheaded New England realist, finds the whole thing absurd. The love between this couple is too deep to have their marriage torn apart by questions of religion, but when the Church moves from New York to Ohio, Mary Ann watches with sadness as friends and family prepare to leave. With simple, deep faith, she turns to the Lord, praying for him to soften Benjamin's heart and help them to be one in this matter as they are in so many others. The Lord answers her prayer in a surprising way, which is only the first step in making her and Benjamin one. (Vol. 2, pp. 117-20, 156-61.)

GOIN' TO ZION   *28*
Men's Chorus

Lyrics by Gerald N. Lund / Music by Lynn S. Lund

In the winter of 1833-34, the Saints in Jackson County, Missouri, the center place of Zion, are driven out by angry mobs. It is a terrible time and carries a terrible cost. Men are whipped, tarred and feathered, and killed. Women and children are driven from their homes into a wintry night barefoot in their night-clothes. Back in Kirtland, God calls upon his Saints to go forth and redeem Zion and help their suffering brothers and sisters. By spring of 1834, "Zion's Camp" is organized. Swelling to over two hundred men, they start the eight-hundred-mile trek westward to fulfill the commandment of the Lord. They quickly find that even though they are on the Lord's errand and going to Zion, it is not a task without its very real challenges—challenges that most of them are able to meet through faith, determination, and even a healthy dose of humor. (Vol. 2, pp. 407-22.)

A MARVELOUS WORK   *33*
Full Choir

Lyrics adapted by Gerald N. Lund from D&C 4 and 18; W. W. Phelps / Music by Lynn S. Lund and Anon.

In response to a direct commandment from the Lord and in spite of their poverty, the Saints begin a temple in Kirtland, Ohio. It will be the first "House of the Lord" built on the earth in many centuries. Finally, in the spring of 1836, the temple is ready for its dedication. The sacrifice of these faithful people is acceptable to God. In a great day of Pentecostal power, the Lord pours out his Spirit upon them. Visions are seen, angels appear, the sound of a mighty rushing wind sweeps over the congregation, and a heavenly glow hovers over the temple itself. The Steeds have been part of that marvelous work which began so simply only a few years before. Now, along with their fellow Saints, they sing their hosannas to God and the Lamb. (Vol. 2, pp. 484-506.)

YOU BROUGHT MY SONG TO LIFE   40
Caroline and Joshua

Lyrics by Gerald N. Lund / Music by Lynn S. Lund

Joshua Steed, the oldest son of Benjamin and Mary Ann, finds Joseph Smith's story of angels and gold plates utterly ridiculous. When he and some friends of rather dubious character attack Joseph in the night and try to steal the plates, Joshua and Benjamin have an angry confrontation and Joshua flees into the night. Drifting west, living hard and drinking hard, Joshua finally ends up in Independence, Missouri. When the Mormons come there and convert his first wife, he becomes part of the mob that drives them out. Sullen, angry, embittered, Joshua even turns his back on his brother and allows him to be whipped unmercifully. But then Joshua makes a trip to Savannah, Georgia, where he meets a beautiful and gracious widow named Caroline Mendenhall. Only after they marry does Caroline learn of this dark, hidden side of Joshua. But her love for him is such that she will not let him dwell there. And Joshua finds that love gradually transforming him. As the months with Caroline turn into years, the hardness softens, the bitterness slowly dissipates, the anger is turned aside. Finally, through Caroline's influence, Joshua makes peace with himself and with his family. (Vol. 3, pp. 245-52, 366-71, 480-84, 525-33.)

TOGETHER, LIFE IS GRAND!   47
Derek and Rebecca

Lyrics by Gerald N. Lund / Music by Lynn S. Lund

After the Church moves to northern Missouri in 1838, Rebecca Steed and Derek Ingalls, an English convert, decide to marry. Derek has been given acreage in a beautiful valley called by the Lord Adam-ondi-Ahman. But when Derek takes his new bride to "Di-Ahman," as the Saints affectionately called it, they find that life in a sod hut is less than wonderful. Never-ending rain leaks in muddy streams through the roof. Mice are plentiful and join them in bed one night. The food is moldy, the hut cold and perpetually damp. One day, Rebecca remembers a scripture which admonishes them to return thanks to God in all things. In a moment, she and Derek are having a contest to see who can enumerate the most things for which they should be grateful. (Vol. 4, pp. 158-61.)

O GOD, WHERE ART THOU?   54
Joseph (in Liberty Jail)

Lyrics adapted by Gerald N. Lund from D&C 121 and 122 /
Music by Lynn S. Lund

In the summer of 1838, the resentment against the Mormons in Missouri again explodes into open warfare. Before it is over, names like DeWitt, Crooked River, Haun's Mill, and Far West will become part of the tragic legacy of the Latter-day Saints. Betrayed into the hands of their enemies by one of their own, Joseph and Hyrum Smith and other Church leaders are marched first to Independence, then to Richmond, and eventually to Liberty, Missouri. There in a dungeon jail, under the most filthy and unbearable of conditions, Joseph languishes for months. And if that were not burden enough, he has to endure the reports that his people, including his own wife and children, are being driven from the state under the harshest of conditions. Finally, in great agony of spirit, he cries out to God, pleading for understanding and for intervention. In one of the great revelations given to man, God answers that tortured cry. Temples are places of revelation. Adapting the words of the Prophet's plea and of God's response found in D&C 121 and 122, the song helps us see why Liberty Jail, that most ironic of names, came to be known as a "temple prison." (Vol. 4, pp. 467-71.)

SOMEDAY I'LL HOLD HIM AGAIN   *61*
Lydia and Joseph

Lyrics adapted by Gerald N. Lund from
Teachings of the Prophet Joseph Smith, *pp. 196-97 / Music by Lynn S. Lund*

After the Saints find refuge in Quincy, Illinois, and Joseph escapes from his imprisonment, within weeks he locates a new place for them—a swampy, mosquito-infested patch of land on a sweeping bend of the Mississippi River. Soon changing its name from Commerce to Nauvoo (a Hebrew word for "beautiful place"), Joseph leads the Saints in the effort to build them a new home. During that first summer of 1839, ague, also called the "shakes," strikes hard among the Saints, who are still terribly weakened from their ordeal in Missouri. Whole families are devastated. Hundreds die. One of those is three-year-old Nathan Joseph Steed, son of Nathan and Lydia Steed. Days later, in what will come to be called "a day of God's power," Joseph rises from his sickbed and goes from house to house healing the sick. This only devastates Lydia further. Why was her son taken? Why couldn't Joseph have come a few days sooner to save him? Why couldn't this boy have lived until the day of power and been spared? Joseph's answer, drawn from his actual teachings, gives solace to all of those who have lost little ones to death. (Vol. 5, pp. 191-94.)

SEASONS OF JOY   *66*
Benjamin and Mary Ann

Lyrics by Gerald N. Lund / Music by Lynn S. Lund

At the marriage of Matthew, their youngest son, Benjamin and Mary Ann look around them. The Steeds have grown to a full clan now. With spouses, grandchildren, and adopted family members, they number almost thirty. More important, after years of separation and sorrow, the family has been reunited. Joshua is one with the family again. Melissa and her family have come to Nauvoo to live. Now with the last of their children leaving their home, it is a time for reflection. Benjamin and Mary Ann rejoice in the great blessings they have been given. Without question, it is truly a season of joy for all. (Vol. 5, pp. 568-75.)

PRAISE TO THE MAN   *73*
Solo (John Taylor) and Full Choir

*Lyrics by James Montgomery and W. W. Phelps /
Music by George Coles and from a Scottish folk song; arranged by Lynn S. Lund*

In the summer of 1844, the mission of Joseph Smith was completed. As the inferno of hatred and bigotry once again engulfed the Saints, Joseph and his dearly beloved Hyrum went to another jail, this time in Carthage, Illinois. This time there would be no escape, no return to their families and friends. On a hot summer afternoon, a mob with painted faces and murderous hearts pounded up the stairs and fired volley after volley into the small bedroom. Hyrum fell first, Joseph a moment later. Thus ended the mission of the Prophet called to open the last dispensation, the man who walked from that grove of trees in 1820 and never looked back. Today we sing our praises to the man who communed with Jehovah, the Prophet and Seer of the Lord. (Vol. 6.)

THE WORK AND THE GLORY
Full Choir

GERALD N. LUND

LYNN S. LUND
MERRILL JENSON

2

shack - les, Bring - ing power to live a - gain.

Great is God's work and great his glo - ry. He works to save and re -

deem all men. He seeks full joy for all his chil - dren,

4

To bring them home with him a-gain.

After cen-tu-ries of dark-ness, Jo-seph knelt on for-est

sod. Blaz-ing pil-lar, blind-ing glo-ry. There be-fore him stood his

6

He works to save and re-deem all men.

He seeks full joy for all his chil - dren,

To bring them home with him a - gain.

Great is his work and his glo - ry.

PILLAR OF LIGHT

Joseph

Adapted by GERALD N. LUND from
Joseph Smith-History 1:14-17

LYNN S. LUND

Where was I to find the truth? And how to know which church was

Soft and gen- tle was the breeze, And warm the sun- light when I

prayed. With - in a sa- cred grove of trees I

asked that I might know the way.

rit.

mf

Dark - ness closed in like the night. De -

accel. *mf*

accel.

struc - tion gath - ered round my soul. Ex - ert - ing all my strength and

f

f

power, I called on God to save my soul.

I saw a pil - lar of light, Ex -

act - ly o - ver my head, A - bove the bright-ness of the sun.

I saw two Be - ings a - bove me,
Stand - ing in the air, Whose glo - ry de - fies de - scrip - tion.
One of them spoke my name, And said, point - ing to the

oth - er: "This is My Be - lov - ed Son. Hear

Him," the Fa - ther said to me.

THIS I KNOW
Lydia

GERALD N. LUND

LYNN S. LUND

Search-ing for an-swers, long-ing for truth.

Wait-ing and wan-d'ring, seek-ing for proof. So man - y voic-es;

18

This I know, there is e - ter - nal life. In my soul I

rit. *f*

have a tes - ti - mo - ny. I know that Je - sus is the Christ.

1.

2.

f

This I know, that God is there and car - ing.

LORD, MAKE US ONE

Mary Ann

GERALD N. LUND

LYNN S. LUND

stub - born man, And make us one. Fa - ther, this is a

de - cent and good- ly man. But blind - ness cov- ers his mind a - bout thy plan.

Fa - ther,— o- pen his eyes to see; I ask on bend- ed knee, Please make us one.

Fa - ther, it is thy gos - pel that pulls me so. Oh, Fa - ther, how can I

stay when my chil - dren go? I know_____ my place is here with him. Give me the

strength with - in. Lord, make us one.

O

Lord,_____ can this be tru - ly_ so? There he lies, teas - ing with his

gen - tle smile, Of- f'ring that for which I dared not hope, To come with me a- cross the long and dis- tant miles. My heart can scarce- ly take it in. Here he is, say- ing that we need not stay. With soft- ened heart he an- swers and then he gives in, And hands to me the thing for which I

prayed.

mp
Fa - ther, hum- bly I kneel a - gain to thee, And thank thee for__ this

an - swer__ to my plea. *mf* Fa - ther,__ I thank thee for this man. Oh, place me

in his hand. Lord, make us one. *f* Fa - ther, how I re -

joice in this gift of thine. I of - fer all that in heart and__ soul is mine.

Fa ther,__ give me the strength with - in To bring my heart to him. Please make us

one. Lord, make us

one.__

GOIN' TO ZION

Men's Chorus

GERALD N. LUND

LYNN S. LUND

29

30

A MARVELOUS WORK
Full Choir

Adapted by GERALD N. LUND
from D&C 4 and 18; W. W. PHELPS

LYNN S. LUND and Anon.

mar - vel-ous work is a - bout to come forth A - mong the chil - dren of men. O

34

ye that em- bark in the serv - ice of God, Serve him with all your heart.

mf

The

field is— white and— read - y to har - vest, And ye are called to the work. So

mf

For

thrust in your sick - le with all of your might. La - bor to do your part.

36

38

YOU BROUGHT MY SONG TO LIFE

Caroline and Joshua

GERALD N. LUND

LYNN S. LUND

You filled me with de - light, When you lis - tened to my tears.

How could I see the hurt and the an - ger, Your deep ag - o - ny?

I was a-fraid That you would push me a-way, Turn-ing from all we had

made.

Joshua
mp

You brought my song to life,____ When I thought no song was

there.

You o-pened up my heart,_____ When you

Stay with me now, Guid - ing me, chid - ing me, Make me this

vow. You are my all, Know - ing me, show - ing me,

Love me and break down the walls.

life,_____ When I thought no song was there._____

You o-pened up my heart, When you taught me_____ how to

care._____

TOGETHER, LIFE IS GRAND!

Derek and Rebecca

GERALD N. LUND

LYNN S. LUND

48

feet!   Mice   in   our   bed!

Leaks   o - ver - head.   Will   it   ev - er   stop   this   rain   -   ing?   There's

mold   on   the   bread.   It's   cold   as   a   shed.   I   can't   be - lieve   she's   not   com -

Rebecca
mf

plain   -   ing.   There's

Derek mf

love my frown- ing, gloom- y, dar- ling spouse! I'm

thank- ful for a wom- an who is blind to all, Who has a nose that can- not smell a

thing. I'm grate - ful that she has a scream that pierc- es steel. That

mouse will nev- er ev - er be the same!

53

O GOD, WHERE ART THOU?

Joseph (in Liberty Jail)

Adapted by GERALD N. LUND
from D&C 121 and 122

LYNN S. LUND

56

from on high speak to me. O my

son, peace be un-to thy soul. Thine af-flic - tions shall be but a small

mo - ment. And if thou en-dure it well, God shall ex -

alt thee on high. Thou shalt tri-umph o - ver

58

all. Art thou great - er than he?

Fear not what man can do. Thou shalt

tri - umph o - ver all thy foes. The Son of

Man hath de - scend - ed be - low them all. Art thou

great - er_____ than he?_____

rit.

SOMEDAY I'LL HOLD HIM AGAIN

Lydia and Joseph

Adapted by GERALD N. LUND
from *Teachings of the Prophet Joseph Smith*, pp. 196-97

LYNN S. LUND

Lydia
mp

Why   is   it   that   lit - tle   chil - dren   Are   tak - en   a -
He   was   Heav'n - ly   Fa - ther's   pre - cious child   Be - fore   he   was

Joseph *mp*

The
All

mo - ment in - fants leave this mor - tal world, They're tak - en to God's
chil - dren are re - deemed by Je - sus Christ, When tak - en home to

keep - ing, In - to e - ter - nal light and glo - ry. Their
Fa - ther's arms, Where they es - cape the sor - rows of this world. They

spir - its are not sleep - ing. They are too
live with God in heav - en. They are too

mf

pure, They are too love - ly To live on this
pure, They are too love - ly To live on this

earth. But some - day we'll hold them a -
earth. But some - day we'll hold them a -

1.
gain.

2.
Lydia Sleep, my ba - by,
Joseph gain.

SEASONS OF JOY

Benjamin and Mary Ann

GERALD N. LUND

LYNN S. LUND

68

joy they bring.

Both
mf

Lord, how we thank thee for fam - 'lies. Some - times we've strug - gled, some -

mp

times we've re - joiced. Dear Lord, we thank thee for grant - ing

a tempo

Sea - sons of sor - row and sea - sons of joy.

mf

Benjamin
mf

Swift - ly the sea - sons are pass - ing, Love deep - 'ning

72

PRAISE TO THE MAN

Solo (John Taylor) and Full Choir

JAMES MONTGOMERY
W. W. PHELPS

GEORGE COLES
SCOTTISH FOLK SONG
Arr. by LYNN S. LUND

74

from dis - guise. The— to - kens in— his hands I knew;— The

Sa - vior stood— be - fore— mine eyes.———————— He—

spake, and my— poor name he named,— "Of me thou hast— not

been a - shamed. These— deeds— shall thy— me - mor - ial be;— Fear

76

78